Mr Tripp
Smells a Rat

SANDY McKAY

ILLUSTRATED BY
RUTH PAUL

WALKER
BOOKS

For little Jed McIntosh.
Also for Blake Simon Wilson
(who always wanted his name in a book).
SM

First published in Great Britain 2013 by Walker Books Ltd
87 Vauxhall Walk, London SE11 5HJ

2 4 6 8 10 9 7 5 3 1

Text © 2011 Sandy McKay
Illustrations © 2011 Ruth Paul

The right of Sandy McKay and Ruth Paul to be identified as author
and illustrator respectively of this work has been asserted by them in
accordance with the Copyright, Designs and Patents Act 1988

This book has been typeset in Bembo Educational

Printed and bound in China

British Library Cataloguing in Publication Data:
a catalogue record for this book is
available from the British Library

ISBN 978-1-4063-5333-4

www.walker.co.uk

Mr Tripp Smells a Rat

Mr Tripp Eats Some Fish

Mr Tripp Finds a Nit

Mr Tripp
Smells a Rat

There are two Ryans in our class. Ryan with the runny nose and the other Ryan.

There are two Sams as well. Girl Sam and boy Sam. And there's Tania and Jessie and Henry and Jamie and Jingjing and Julie and Jasper and Ted. And then there's me – Lily.

Our teacher's name is Mr Tripp. Mr Tripp is awesome.

He is round like a teddy bear and he wears a red shirt that comes out over his tummy.

The things Mr Tripp likes are:
chocolate muffins, surprise spelling tests
and riddles.

The things Mr Tripp doesn't like
are: sardine sandwiches, litterbugs and
knock-knock jokes. Oh, and one other
thing – RATS!

Mr Tripp hates rats.

"Good morning,
Room Five."

"Good morning, Mr Tripp."

"What's brown and hairy,
wears dark glasses and carries a pile
of exercise books?"

"What?"

"A coconut disguised as a teacher."

Mr Tripp is good at telling jokes.
He says everyone has something
they are good at.

This is what the kids in Room
Five are good at. Jingjing can turn
her eyelids inside out. Julie can juggle
oranges (three at the same time!)
Ted can balance on one leg for
85 seconds without falling over.

Jasper knows the first verse of
"Waltzing Matilda" backwards.
Jessie can do a cartwheel with one
hand. I can hold my breath for
ages. And Jamie is good at
drawing frogs.

11

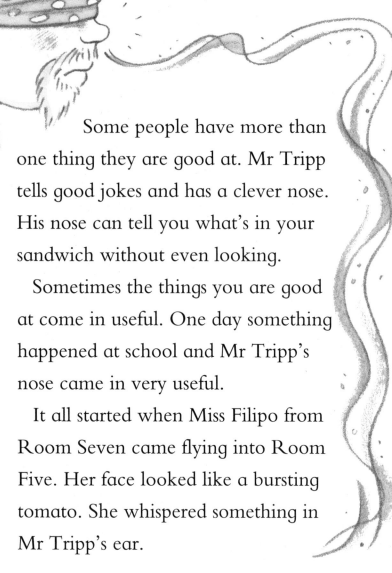

Some people have more than one thing they are good at. Mr Tripp tells good jokes and has a clever nose. His nose can tell you what's in your sandwich without even looking.

Sometimes the things you are good at come in useful. One day something happened at school and Mr Tripp's nose came in very useful.

It all started when Miss Filipo from Room Seven came flying into Room Five. Her face looked like a bursting tomato. She whispered something in Mr Tripp's ear.

"Are you sure?" he said.

"Yes," said Miss Filipo. "I'm sure."

"Well, then," said Mr Tripp. "I better see what I can do."

But he looked like he didn't want
to do anything.

So Miss Filipo told everyone from
Room Five and Room Seven to
assemble in the playground. "Nice and
quietly. No pushing and shoving."

It was just like a fire drill.

"Why are we doing this?" I asked.

14

"'Cause there's been an escape,"
said Sophie from Room Seven.

"An escape?"

"Yes. Ricky Rider's rat sneaked out of
its cage and no one knows where it went."

"And Miss Filipo is scared of rats.
So that's why Mr Tripp has to catch it,"
said Sophie.

"Oh," I said.

15

If you stand on the lunch seats
outside, you can see right into the
classrooms.

Jamie and I watched Mr Tripp walk into Room Seven, get down on his hands and knees ... and crawl around the floor...

"What's Mr Tripp doing?" asked Jingjing.
"He looks like our cat does when she's trying to catch a mouse," said Jamie.

"Shhh," said Miss Filipo. "He's smelling a rat."

17

"But Mr Tripp doesn't like rats,"
I said.

"Neither do I," said Miss Filipo.

And just then something really
funny happened. Mr Tripp jumped
up onto a desk and started yelling,
"Aaaaaahhhhh!!!" And he waved his
arms about and pointed.

18

Then Miss Filipo went running in
with a cage going, "Where? Where?
Where?"

And Mr Tripp shouted, "Over there."

And Miss Filipo raced over. And the
next minute something white and furry
was crawling into the cage.

20

And then Ricky started jumping
up and down saying, "Yay. Mr Tripp
found my rat." And he went racing
in as well.

And then Mr Tripp came out with
sweat pouring off his forehead.

And Miss Filipo asked Mr Tripp
if he was OK.

And Mr Tripp said, yes, he was, but
Jamie didn't think he looked it.

And Miss Filipo said, "Thank you
so much. You are very brave."

And then she turned to us and said,
"Three cheers for Mr Tripp."

And we all shouted, "Hip hip hooray."

And then Jasper said in a little quiet voice, "Mr Tripp doesn't look very brave to me."

And Julie said, "Yeah. If Mr Tripp is so brave, then how come he's frightened of a measly little rat?"

And Jingjing said, "Perhaps being scared of something is the thing that makes you brave."

And Miss Filipo said, "I think you're right, Jingjing."

And then Mr Tripp told us another joke.

"What's purple and white, lives in the sea and has big teeth?"

"What?"

"The grape white shark."

And we all went back to class and sat at our desks and waited for the bell to ring.

Mr Tripp Eats Some Fish

"Good morning, Room Five."

"Good morning, Mr Tripp."

Mr Tripp looked funny. He had his finger on his nose and was trying to go cross-eyed.

"Did you hear about the cross-eyed teacher?"

"No."

"He had no control over his pupils."

Everyone laughed except for girl Sam, who usually takes a while to get the joke.

Today Mr Tripp was wearing a new shirt.

"You've got a new shirt," said Ryan with the runny nose.

"So I have," said Mr Tripp. "Can anyone guess why I've got a new shirt?"

"Is it your birthday?" I asked.

"No. That's next Friday."

"Did you lose the other one?" said boy Sam.

"No. I'll give you a clue, shall I?"
Then Mr Tripp patted his tummy.
"I had to get a new shirt for a special
reason."

Still no one could guess. So Mr Tripp
tried a riddle. "What is good to lose
and not so good to gain?"

Everyone looked blank. So Mr
Tripp patted his tummy again.

This time Jessie put up her hand.
"I know. I know," she said.

"Yes, Jessie?"

"It's your fat tummy. You lost your fat tummy and had to buy a smaller shirt."

Mr Tripp grinned because Jessie was right. Even when you looked really hard you couldn't see his fat tummy.

"How did you lose it?" asked Henry.

"I went on a diet," said Mr Tripp.

"A diet?" said Henry.

"A seafood diet, actually."

"What does that mean?"

"It means you have to eat lots of fish."

"Is that all?"

"And lots of fruit and vegetables. And no chips or lollies or chocolate," said Mr Tripp.

"No chocolate? That's not fair," said Jingjing.

"Fish is good for you," I said.

"So it is," said Mr Tripp.

"It doesn't taste as good as chocolate though," said Jasper.

"No," said Mr Tripp. "Not quite as good as chocolate."

Jasper thought we should
have a party for Mr Tripp's birthday.
"That's a good idea," said Tania.

33

"I can bring the balloons," I said.

"And I can make a cake," said Ted.

"It will have to be a fish cake," said Jingjing.

"A fish cake?"

"For Mr Tripp's seafood diet."

"Oh yeah," said Ted, looking a bit disappointed.

We couldn't wait for it to be Friday.

Friday came, and when Mr Tripp walked into class we all jumped out from behind our desks and went,

"Surprise!"

34

Then we had a party where everyone
showed off the thing they were good at.

Jingjing turned her eyelids inside
out. Julie juggled oranges. Ted
balanced on his leg for 85 seconds
without falling over. Jasper sang the

first verse of "Waltzing Matilda"
backwards. Jessie did a cartwheel
with one hand. I held my breath
for ages and ages. And Jamie
made a lovely card with
frogs on it.

After we'd finished, Mr Tripp said
he was amazed at our wide range
of talents.

"This is the best birthday ever," he
said. "Room Five is a clever class."

"There's one more thing," said Ted.
And off he raced to get the cake, which
was sitting on a plate in the boys'
cloakroom.

"I bet you can't guess what it is,"
he said, when he got back.

"Can you give me a clue?" said Mr
Tripp.

Ted thought for a minute.
"What is brown and pink and comes
from the sea?" he said.

Mr Tripp thought for a moment. "A rainbow trout?"

"No. That comes from a river," said Jasper, who knows all about fishing.

"So it does," said Mr Tripp. "I give up."

So Ted took the tea towel off the plate and went,

"Tada!"

And Mr Tripp laughed and laughed
because guess what was underneath.

(You won't so I'll tell you.)

It was a stack of chocolate fish
all piled up like a cake.

"Wowee! A chocolate fish cake!
What a clever idea."

There were 27 chocolate fish. One
for each of us and one for Mr Tripp.

"It's the perfect thing for a seafood diet," said Mr Tripp, biting off a tail.

Then we all sang "Happy Birthday" and sat at our desks and waited for the bell to ring.

Mr Tripp
Finds a Nit

"Good morning, Room Five."

"Good morning, Mr Tripp."

"Why wouldn't the little skeleton do his homework?" he asked.

"I don't know."

"Because he was a lazy bones.

"Today we need to talk about something important," said Mr Tripp, putting on his serious face. "We have a problem in Room Five and I've been scratching my head over what to do about it." Mr Tripp walked up and down in front of his desk. "Does anyone know what I'm talking about?"

No one put up their hand. So Mr
Tripp scratched his head and drew
something on the board. "What's got
a head, a pair of antennae, two body
segments, and six legs?"

"An alien from outer
space," I said.

48

"No," said Mr Tripp.

"An insect," said Tania.

"Very good," said Mr Tripp.

"Is it a spider?" said girl Sam.

"A spider's not an insect," said Jessie.

"Why is a spider not an insect?"

"Because it's got eight legs," said Jingjing.

49

"That's right. Does anyone know what type of insect this is?" asked Mr Tripp.

"A beetle?"

"No."

"A stick insect?"

"No."

"A mosquito?"

"No. I'll give you a clue. This insect likes to live in people's hair."

"I know," said Jasper. "It's a nit."

"Very good, Jasper," said Mr Tripp. "Actually, a nit is what the egg is called. The insect is a louse. Head lice like to live in people's hair."

Suddenly, everyone started scratching because when you talk about things living in your hair it makes you itchy.

"Oh, yuck," said Julie. "I don't want insects living in *my* hair."

"That's why we need to get rid of them," said Mr Tripp.

After lunch Mr Tripp gave us all
a handout. "Here are some instructions
for treating head lice," he said.
"Remember, there's absolutely nothing
to be embarrassed about. And the
important thing is to get onto it
straightaway."

So every day, just before the bell went,
Mr Tripp said, "Don't forget to treat
your nits."

And every day we went home to do
the things we needed to do to keep
away the nits.

Two weeks later Mr Tripp had a look
to see if the plan had worked. We all
stood in a line with our heads down.

"I know a joke," said Ted.

"Where do insects do their shopping?"

"Where?"

"At the flea market."

Everyone laughed – even girl Sam.

When Mr Tripp had finished
checking he said, "You've all done very
well. I haven't found a single louse."
And then he gave us each a sticker and
a lollipop.

"Three cheers for Room Five," said Mr Tripp.

And we all shouted, "Hip hip hooray."

But then Jingjing put up her hand and said, "I think you've forgotten someone."

Mr Tripp looked at his class roll. "No. I don't think so."

"What about you?" she said.

Mr Tripp scratched his head. "That's a good point, Jingjing. So who would like to check my head?"

"I will," said Jamie. And up she went to the front of the class. And then something really funny happened. Jamie found an insect in Mr Tripp's hair. It was so small you could hardly see it. But it made his face go all pink. Everyone tried not to laugh.

"Oh, my goodness," said Mr Tripp.
"So that's why I've been scratching my
head so much."

"Remember, it's nothing to be
embarrassed about," said Jamie.
"The important thing is to get onto it
straightaway."

"Yes. Thank you, Jamie," said Mr
Tripp. "Thank you very much."
    And we all sat at our desks and
waited for the bell to ring.

More of Mr Tripp's Favourite Riddles

Question: What has a tongue
but can't talk?

Answer: A shoe.

Question: What has teeth but no mouth?

Answer: A saw.